CELLO

STARTERS FOR CELLO

MICHAEL ROSE

ROMANCE

GAVOTTE

EVENING SONG

PASTORALE

PROCESSION

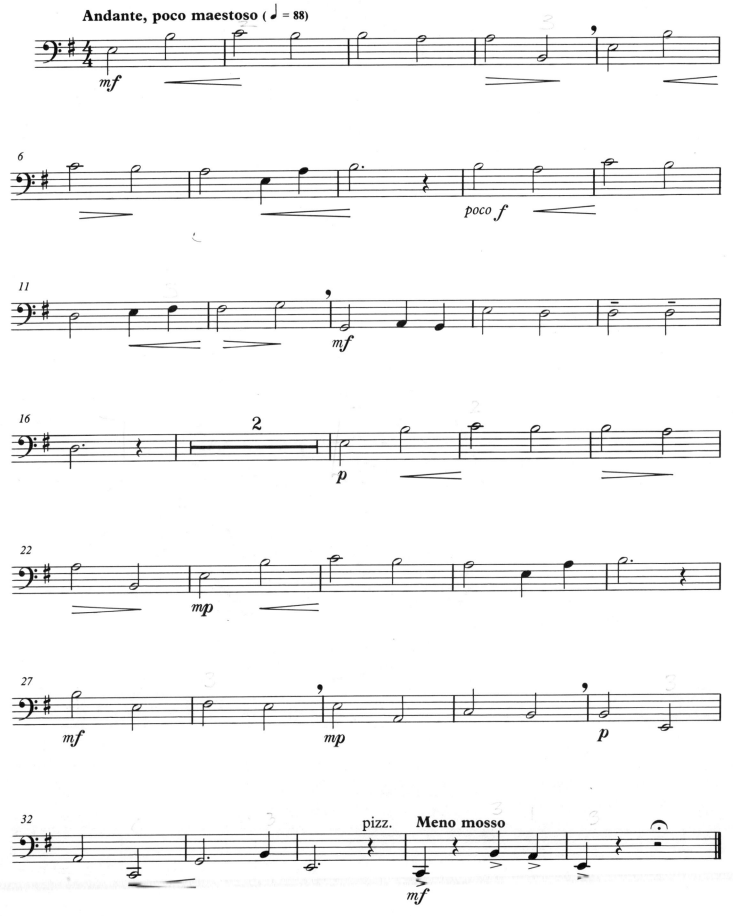

MARCH

CELLO

BERCEUSE

MELANCHOLY SONG

SERENADE

VALSE

STARTERS FOR CELLO

Ten original pieces
with piano accompaniment

MICHAEL ROSE

**THE ASSOCIATED BOARD OF
THE ROYAL SCHOOLS OF MUSIC**

CONTENTS

STARTERS FOR CELLO

MICHAEL ROSE

ROMANCE

GAVOTTE

EVENING SONG

PASTORALE

Piacevole – molto legato (♩ = 90-94)

PROCESSION

14

MARCH

AB 2069

BERCEUSE

MELANCHOLY SONG

Andantino semplice (♩ = 72)

SERENADE

VALSE

Dal segno al Fine